20 Answers

&

Faith
& Science

Trent Horn

Catholic
Answers
Press

20 Answers: Faith & Science
Trent Horn
© 2014 Catholic Answers

Published by Catholic Answers, Inc.
2020 Gillespie Way
El Cajon, California 92020
1-888-291-8000 orders
619-387-0042 fax
catholic.com

Printed in the United States of America

ISBN 978-1-938983-87-0
ISBN 978-1-938983-88-7 Kindle
ISBN 978-1-938983-89-4 ePub

Introduction

Didn't the Catholic Church ban science in the Middle Ages in order to protect the Faith? Wasn't Galileo tortured for proving the Church was wrong about the sun orbiting the Earth? Didn't Columbus bravely defy a Church that believed he would sail off the edge of a flat planet?

These and many other myths about the relationship between the Catholic Church and science are just that: myths. In fact, you can find the origins for many of them in two books written more than a hundred years ago: Andrew Dickson White's *A History of the Warfare of Science with Theology in Christendom* (1896) and John Draper's *History of the Conflict between Religion and Science* (1874).

Today, historians have largely abandoned the conclusions reached by Draper and White, who promoted what is now called "the conflict thesis," the belief that science and religion are at odds. In the book *Science and Religion: A Historical Introduction*, science historian Colin Russell writes, "The conflict thesis, at least in its simple form, is now widely perceived as a wholly inadequate intellectual framework within which to construct a sensible and realistic historiography of Western science. . . . At different phases of their history, science and religion were not so much at war as largely independent, mutually encouraging, or even symbiotic."[1]

Unfortunately, as Mark Twain said, "A lie can travel halfway around the world while the truth is still putting on its shoes." The purpose of this booklet is to help the truth catch up to the lies about the Catholic Church and to show that there is no contradiction in worshipping the God who created the universe and in using science to explore and understand that creation.

1. Didn't the Catholic Church condemn science and as a result send us into the medieval "Dark Ages"?[2]

According to this myth, after Christianity went from being a persecuted cult to being the official religion of the Roman Empire, the Catholic Church refused to tolerate the freethinking nature of pagan philosophers and scientists. Following St. Paul's exhortation to spurn "the wisdom of the wise," Christians burned down the famous library of Alexandria and murdered the library director's daughter, an intelligent and beautiful pagan mathematician named Hypatia.

However, the evidence from history tells a different story about Hypatia and the library of Alexandria. According to Church historian Socrates of Constantinople, in A.D. 415 a mob in Alexandria did kill Hypatia, but it was because she was caught in a power struggle between St. Cyril, the bishop of Alexandria, and Orestes, the governor of Egypt. At that time, Alexandria contained large numbers of Christians, Jews, and pagans.

Violent riots between these groups were common (see Acts 19:29-40 for a description of a similar riot in Ephesus), and the uneasy relationship between St. Cyril and Orestes did little to quell them.

Socrates describes the murder of Hypatia at the hands of a mob led by a lector named Peter the reader. The mob's motive was to remove what seemed to be the only obstacle to Orestes and Cyril's reconciliation, that being Orestes's friendship with Hypatia. While this episode reflects poorly on the character of some Alexandrian Christians, it is not indicative of a widespread attempt to silence pagan scientists. Science historian David Lindberg writes, "[Hypatia's] death had everything to do with local politics and virtually nothing to do with science."[3] Even though he was antagonistic toward Cyril in his writings, Socrates also never places the blame for the riot on St. Cyril or the Church.[4]

What about the charge that fanatical Christians burned down the famous library of Alexandria, resulting in the loss of hundreds of thousands of classical works? All we know for certain about the library is that it was built in Egypt during the third or second century B.C. and was one of the largest libraries in the world. Although some, such as Carl Sagan in his book *Cosmos,* imply that a Christian mob burned down the library after the murder of Hypatia, there is no historical account prior to the eighteenth century that makes this accusation.[5]

Indeed, the ancient primary sources describe the library's being destroyed multiple times in the centuries prior to the murder of Hypatia. The first destruction came in 47 B.C. when Julius Caesar besieged Alexandria. According to the ancient historian Plutarch, "[W]hen the enemy endeavored to cut off his communication by sea, he was forced to divert that danger by setting fire to his own ships, which, after burning the docks, thence spread on and destroyed the great library."[6] The second destruction most likely came in A.D. 273 when the Roman emperor Aurelian invaded Egypt and burned most of the city of Alexandria to the ground.

Another part of this myth claims that after the library's destruction, the Western world fell into the Dark Ages because the Church persecuted and suppressed scientific discovery. For example, Sagan asks why Western civilization "slumber[ed] through a thousand years of darkness" after the fall of Rome. He proposes the theory that science simply had no practical application for people, and so its practice fell into disfavor until Columbus and Copernicus rediscovered its usefulness in the sixteenth century.[7]

But Sagan is wrong. Four hundred years before Copernicus and Columbus, the Catholic Church gave rise to the institution that became the primary source for knowledge in our modern world: the university. Beginning in Paris and Bologna in the year 1200, universities supported scholars like St. Thomas Aquinas, who developed a synthesis of classical Greco-Roman knowledge and Christian theology.

Within a few centuries, more than fifty universities sprang up throughout Europe, providing hundreds of thousands of students with unprecedented access to knowledge about science and history. According to science historian Michael Shank, "If the medieval Church had intended to discourage or suppress science, it certainly made a colossal mistake in tolerating—to say nothing of supporting—the university."[8]

So why was there no apparent scientific progress between the fifth and thirteenth centuries? One reason is that Western civilization was still reeling from the destruction of the Roman Empire. With the loss of stability that followed the destruction of Rome, the Catholic Church became the protector of civilization. Monasteries across Europe copied what precious ancient manuscripts survived Rome's fall, and this in turn preserved the history and collected knowledge of the past. In contrast to the idea that the Middle Ages represented intellectual stagnation, the eighth century saw the development of Carolingian miniscule.[9] This new form of handwriting was simpler to learn and far easier to read, thus allowing more manuscripts to be copied. This included copies of ancient works discovered in the Middle East that helped spur the growth of scholastic thought in Europe during the late Middle Ages.

2. Did the Catholic Church teach that the Earth was flat?

Another popular myth claims that well into the Middle Ages Christians believed that the Earth was flat. Part of the legend even includes priests and other Christians warning Christopher Columbus that he should not tempt God by trying to sail around the world, since he would only fall off the edge of a flat Earth. But is this really what happened?

In the fifth and sixth centuries before Christ, most Greek scholars accepted the view that Earth was a sphere. This explained its curved shadow on the moon, and why a ship descends below the horizon as it goes out to sea. In fact, in the second century Eratosthenes of Cyrene calculated the Earth's circumference at about 85 percent of its actual distance. The ancient Roman historian and scientist Pliny the Elder wrote in A.D. 79, "Everyone agrees that it has the most perfect figure. We always speak of the ball of the Earth, and we admit it to be a globe bounded by the poles."[10]

Although some Church Fathers like Lactantius believed the Earth was flat, it was not the majority view, nor was it ever a required view for orthodoxy. St. Basil the Great went so far as to say that whatever the shape of the Earth was, it would not detract from his appreciation for the creation. He said that Moses, the author of Genesis, "has passed over in silence, as useless, all that is unimportant for us,"[11] e.g., the issue of the Earth's shape.

Even Andrew Dickson White, the premier nineteenth-century promoter of the "conflict thesis" between the Church and science, noted the belief that the Earth is a sphere: "Clement of Alexandria and Origen had even supported it. Ambrose and Augustine had tolerated it. . . . Eminent authorities in later ages, such as Albert the Great, St. Thomas Aquinas, Dante, and Vincent of Beauvais, felt obliged to accept the doctrine of the Earth's sphericity, and as we approach the modern period we find its truth acknowledged by the vast majority of thinking men."[12] Science historians David Lindberg and Ronald Numbers conclude, "[T]here was scarcely a Christian scholar of the Middle Ages who did not acknowledge [the Earth's] sphericity and even know its approximate circumference."[13]

So what is the source of the flat Earth myth? The idea that Columbus faced opposition to his voyage to the New World from clergy who denied the Earth is round comes from a fictional scene in Washington Irving's *A History of the Life and Voyages of Christopher Columbus* (1828), one of the first examples of American historical fiction. In reality, the major conflict between Columbus and those who criticized his plan to sail to the New World concerned the length of the trip, not the shape of the Earth. Columbus grossly underestimated the circumference of the Earth but was fortunate to find the New World where he thought he would find Eastern Asia.

Irving's romanticized portrait of Columbus, with all its historical inaccuracies, found its way into the hands of nineteenth-century rationalist opponents of the Church. They used the story to characterize the opponents of Darwinian evolution as uncritical simpletons whose denial of evolution could be likened to medieval Christianity's supposed denial of a spherical Earth.

In addition, the nineteenth-century agnostic Robert Ingersoll attributed the following fictional quotation to the sixteenth-century explorer Magellan: "The church says the earth is flat; but I have seen its shadow on the moon, and I have more confidence even in a shadow than in the church."[14] If, as we have seen, the Church in Columbus's time did not promote a flat Earth, it's extremely unlikely it did so thirty years later during Magellan's expeditions. According to science historian James Hannam, "Atheists and agnostics championed the conflict thesis for their own purposes, but historical research gradually demonstrated that Draper and White had propagated more fantasy than fact in their efforts to prove that science and religion are locked in eternal conflict."[15]

3. Did the Catholic Church condemn human dissection and so stifle understanding of the human body?

According to Andrew Dickson White, "[T]he formula known as the Apostles' Creed had, in its teachings regarding the resurrection of the body, supplanted the doctrine laid down by St. Paul. Thence came a dread of mutilating the body in such a way that some injury might result to its final resurrection at the Last Day, and additional reasons for hindering dissections in the study of anatomy."[16] White claims that this opposition can be found in a papal decree from Pope Boniface VIII as well as in a decree from the Council of Le Mans that forbade monks from performing surgery.

The idea that the Catholic Church would stifle life-saving medical research because of its adherence to archaic religious doctrine is also a favorite piece of rhetoric among those who defend embryonic stem cell research (see question 17). During a U.S. Senate debate on funding stem-cell research, former Senator Arlen Specter of Pennsylvania said, "Pope Boniface VII [sic] banned the practice of cadaver dissection in the 1200s. This stopped the practice for 300 years and greatly slowed the accumulation of education regarding human anatomy. Finally, in the 1500s, Michael Servetus used cadaver dissection to study blood circulation. He was tried and imprisoned by the Catholic Church."[17]

Specter and White erred on a number of points relating to the medieval Church's position on human dissection. First, prior to the fourteenth century there was little to no interest in dissecting humans in order to study them. Most people recognized that corpses were a source of disease, and there were many local customs not related to Catholic teaching that promoted speedy and honorable burial for the dead.

Around the year 1300, students at the Italian university in Bologna acquired access to the recently translated works of second-century Roman physician Galen. This prompted them to study human anatomy through dissection, and a textbook based on their work was published. Even the personal physician of three popes, Guy de Chauliac, used dissection to gain knowledge for surgeries. He is reported to have said, "A surgeon who does not know his anatomy is like a blind man carving a log."[18]

So what are we to make of White's and Specter's evidence for an ecclesial ban on dissection? It is true, as White says, that in 1248 the Council of Le Mans banned clergy from performing surgery. But this was not because dissection was considered evil; the ban was meant to protect clergy members from being involved in hazardous surgeries that could damage their reputations were the surgeries botched.

White is also correct that Pope Boniface VIII (not the invalid antipope Boniface VII, whom Specter cited) issued a papal bull called *De Sepulturis* that prohibited the cutting up of human bodies, but the bull had nothing to do with dissection—it only prohibited the abuse of corpses. *De Sepulturis* stated, "Persons cutting up the bodies of the dead, barbarously cooking them in order that the bones being separated from the flesh may be carried for burial into their own countries, are by the very fact excommunicated." Municipalities and public universities continued public dissections after the proclamation of the bull. A practitioner of dissection would find himself in trouble with the law only if he *stole* the bodies he used from local graveyards.[19]

Finally, the Catholic Church did not imprison the Spanish heretic Michael Servetus because he practiced dissection. It was Servetus's denial of the Trinity and other key Christian beliefs that brought ecclesial condemnation upon him.[20] Servetus was so despised that the Protestant Reformer John Calvin sent the Roman Catholic Church evidence to convict him. After Servetus escaped custody and fled to Geneva, it was Calvin—not the Catholic Church—who had him executed for the crime of heresy.

4. If the Church was so hospitable to science, then why did it kill the ingenious scientist Giordano Bruno?

In the Campo de Fiori neighborhood of Rome there is a statue of a mysterious figure draped in a hood, staring solemnly into the distance. The statue is of the sixteenth-century Dominican friar and natural scientist Giordano Bruno, and the newly unified kingdom of Italy erected it in 1889 after Italy seized control of Rome from the pope. The new Roman municipal government commissioned the statue in commemoration of Bruno, a fellow opponent of the Church, and it was situated on the site where he had been burned at the stake nearly 300 years earlier. Those who promote the conflict thesis like to portray Bruno as "the first martyr for science"[21] and claim that his promotion of heliocentrism, or the belief that the Earth revolves around the sun, led to Bruno's execution by Church officials.

Andrew Dickson White describes the saga of Bruno this way: "This new warrior was that strange mortal, Giordano Bruno. He was hunted from land to land, until at last he turned on his pursuers with fearful invectives. For this he was entrapped at Venice, imprisoned during six years in the dungeons of the Inquisition at Rome, then burned alive, and his ashes scattered to the winds. Still, the new truth lived on. Ten years after the martyrdom of Bruno the truth of Copernicus's doctrine was established by the telescope of Galileo."[22]

But the true story is not so simple.

At the age of seventeen Bruno joined the Dominican Order and became known for his excellent memory as well as his penchant for pushing the limits of orthodoxy. He became enamored with the writings of ancient philosophers, and when he was about to be investigated by the Inquisition for allegations that he was defending Arianism, he fled Italy. In 1591, Giovanni Mocenigo, a member of a wealthy Venetian family who wanted Bruno to instruct him in the art of memory, invited him to return.

But when the relationship between them soured, Mocenigo reported Bruno to the Roman Inquisition, which then prosecuted Bruno for his heretical beliefs. The trial records show that Bruno was not tried for his belief in the Copernican model of the solar system. According to the *Stanford Encyclopedia of Philosophy*, "[I]n 1600 there was no official Catholic position on the Copernican system, and it was certainly not a heresy. When [Bruno] was burned at the stake as a heretic, it had nothing to do with his writings in support of Copernican cosmology."[23]

The closest thing to a cosmological belief that was condemned was Bruno's belief in the "plurality of worlds," that is, the belief that an unknown number of inhabited planets besides Earth existed throughout an infinite universe. Such a belief clashed with the Church's teaching about the uniqueness of Adam's sin as well as the efficacy of Christ's sacrifice. However, this charge against Bruno represented neither the Church's trying to place controls on scientific investigation nor the subversion of an objective scientific truth (such as the truth of the Earth's rotation). Scientists have yet to discover (and may never discover) extraterrestrial life, and sixteenth-century speculation on the issue belonged to the realm of philosophy, not science.

The *Catholic Encyclopedia* affirms that "Bruno was not condemned for his defense of the Copernican system of astronomy, nor for his doctrine of the plurality of inhabited worlds, but for his theological errors, among which were the following: that Christ was not God but merely an unusually skillful magician, that the Holy Ghost is the soul of the world, that the Devil will be saved, etc."[24]

5. Why did the Church torture and imprison Galileo for his belief that the Earth revolved around the sun?

The case of Galileo Galilei is perhaps the most-cited example of the supposed conflict between the Catholic Church and modern science. In his book *A Brief History of Time*, physicist Stephen Hawking recounts an audience he had with Pope John Paul II, during which, he claims, the pope said scientists "should not inquire into the Big Bang itself because that was the moment of creation and therefore the work of God."[25] Hawking joked that he did not want to share his research about the beginning of the universe for fear of being "handed over to the inquisition." He then likened his work to Galileo's and noted that he was born exactly 300 years after Galileo died.

Critics like Hawking usually describe the Galileo affair as follows: Galileo diligently studied astronomy and came to the conclusion that the Earth rotated on its axis and orbited a stationary sun (a view now known as heliocentrism). The Church, aghast that Galileo had disproven the biblical view that the sun revolved around the Earth (geocentrism), tortured and imprisoned Galileo until he recanted his heretical belief.

As with almost all the stories used to support the conflict thesis, this one is oversimplified. First, the Catholic Church did not condemn the heliocentric view of the universe. Copernicus's major work defending heliocentrism, *On the Revolution of the Celestial Orbs*, was published ninety years before Galileo's trial and was even dedicated to Pope Paul III.[26] Second, geocentrism was not the default view among theologians simply because it was a revealed truth found in Scripture. They accepted it because it was also the default view among scientists at the time. They simply accepted the arguments Aristotle had previously made against the heliocentric theory 2,000 years earlier.

Aristotle argued that, if the Earth were rotating around the sun, we should notice a shift in the location of the stars, because we would be viewing them from different locations during the Earth's orbit. This is called a parallax shift, and something similar can be seen if you hold your index finger about eighteen inches in front of your eyes and look at it in alternating sequence one eye at a time. Your finger appears to shift location based on with which eye you view it. A similar change among the stars should be visible if we observe the stars at different points during the Earth's orbit. While parallax shift can be observed today with special instruments, the stars were too far away for a parallax shift to be observed in Galileo's time.

Still, Galileo's theory had promise. Pope Urban VIII met with him and urged Galileo to publish arguments for and against his theory but not to teach it as being an established truth. However, Galileo later wrote *Dialogue on the Two World Systems,* in which a character named *Simplicio,* or simpleton, voiced the pope's arguments. This tweaking of the papal nose, coupled with Galileo's bold assertion that Scripture would have to be reinterpreted in light of his findings, resulted in Galileo's famous trial in 1633.

Contrary to popular belief, Galileo was not tortured but was found to be "vehemently under suspicion of heresy." According to the Tuscan ambassador to Niccolini, Galileo was placed under house arrest but was even given a servant to attend to him until he died of old age.[27]

Under the leadership of Pope John Paul II, the Catholic Church apologized for any injustices done to Galileo. Pope John Paul reflected on Galileo in an address to the Pontifical Academy of Sciences. After calling the affair a "sad misunderstanding," he said, "Thanks to his intuition as a brilliant physicist and by relying on different arguments, Galileo, who practically invented the experimental method, understood why only the sun could function as the center of the world, as it was then known, that is to say, as a planetary system. The error of the theologians of the time, when they maintained the centrality of the Earth, was to think that our understanding of the physical world's structure was, in some way, imposed by the literal sense of Sacred Scripture."[28]

Some critics maintain that the Galileo affair proves the Church and the pope are not infallible. However, neither an ecumenical council nor any pope speaking *ex cathedra* ever declared Galileo to be in error or the geocentric system to be the correct astronomical model of the universe. The Church does not teach that the verdict of a tribunal, which is what took place during Galileo's trial, can be considered to reflect infallible Church teaching.

Finally, Galileo's theory was wrong, because he believed the planets orbited the sun in a perfect circle, whereas the planets actually have an elliptical orbit. Because of this, Galileo's theory could not account for all astronomical observations, and that is one reason why the Church urged caution regarding it. This is, in fact, why the Catholic Church limits the scope of its authority to judge infallibly only matters related to faith or morals and does not infallibly endorse scientific theories, which have the tendency, no matter how well supported at the time, to be overturned in later centuries.

6. Doesn't the concept of faith, or believing without evidence, contradict the concept of reason, which means to follow the evidence where it leads?

According to the *Catechism*, "Though faith is above reason, there can never be any real discrepancy between faith and reason. Since the same God who reveals mysteries and infuses faith has bestowed the light of reason on the human mind, God cannot deny himself, nor can truth ever contradict truth. Consequently, methodical research in all branches of knowledge, provided it is carried out in a truly scientific manner and does not override moral laws, can never conflict with the faith, because the things of the world and the things of faith derive from the same God."[29] John Paul II beautifully illustrated the harmony between faith and reason in the opening lines of his encyclical *Fides et Ratio*. He wrote that faith and reason are "two wings on which the human spirit rises to the contemplation of truth."

A conflict between faith and reason arises only when people use incorrect definitions of these terms. It is true that reason involves the use of the mind to make sense of the world and justify the beliefs we think are true. However, faith is not "believing without evidence" or "belief in the absence of evidence." According to paragraph 1814 of the *Catechism*, faith is "the theological virtue by which we believe in God and believe all that he has said and revealed to us." Unfortunately, we live in a culture that equates faith with blindly accepting something as true. It may be more helpful to think of faith as a kind of trust based on good reasons.

For example, by reason you know that a plane is capable of flying, but you have "faith"—i.e., belief that cannot be proven directly—that any particular plane is able to fly. You trust—but you don't *absolutely know*—that the plane is maintained properly and the pilot is actually a pilot and not a Pilates instructor. Now, with some diligence you could corroborate these beliefs, but there are other beliefs that we must simply accept with faith-like trust. These include the belief that the laws of physics will not change suddenly mid-flight, causing the plane to crash. Such a belief cannot be proven but must simply be assumed.

Skeptics may gloat that when reason and faith conflict—especially in the area of science—it is always faith that must accommodate the findings of science. But this is not always true. When science claims that the best way to study the spread of syphilis is to inject impoverished minorities with placebo vaccines and lie about the treatment these people were receiving (as occurred between 1932 and 1972 in the Tuskegee syphilis experiments), it is science that has erred. It must change and accommodate the religious truth that you should "love your neighbor as yourself" and not use people in the same way you would use laboratory guinea pigs.

Or consider another example. For hundreds of years scientists committed to naturalism believed that the universe was eternal, while the Bible and the Church taught that the universe had a beginning in time.[30] Instead of the Faith accommodating science, it turns out that science may have to accommodate the Faith, as new evidence from Big Bang cosmology points toward an ultimate beginning of the universe. As former NASA scientist Robert Jastrow writes, "For the scientist who has lived by his faith in the power of reason, the story ends like a bad dream. He has scaled the mountain of ignorance; he is about to conquer the highest peak; as he pulls himself over the final rock, he is greeted by a band of theologians who have been sitting there for centuries."[31]

7. Why can't I just have faith in science as the way to understand the world?

During the Middle Ages, science was defined as "the knowledge of things from their causes."[32] Under Aquinas's definition, even theology was considered a science, because it involved a quest for knowledge (Latin, *sciencia*). However, after the work of modern thinkers such as Isaac Newton and Galileo Galilei, the concept of "science" shrank to accommodate what had once been called natural philosophy, or natural science. In 1837 William Whewell coined the term *scientist* to describe a person who seeks systematic explanations for observed phenomena.

Science is a helpful tool when it comes to understanding the world, but it's not the *only* tool we use to understand the world, any more than a hammer is the only tool you use to build a house. The danger we face today is that both professional scientists and a growing number of laypeople rely on science to be the sole arbiter of truth. Physicists Stephen Hawking and Leonard Mlodinow wrote in their 2009 book *The Grand Design*, "What is the nature of reality? Where did all this come from? Did the universe need a creator? Traditionally, these are questions for philosophy, but philosophy is dead. Philosophy has not kept up with modern developments in science, especially physics. Scientists have become the bearers of the torch of discovery in our quest for knowledge."[33]

But the torch of science can't illuminate the answer to every question we have about the world. For example, science relies on philosophy in order to know what science even is, how science works, and what counts as science. It is philosophy that helps distinguish the legitimate sciences of astronomy and chemistry from the pseudo-sciences of astrology and alchemy. Science also relies on the philosophical assumption that the world operates under scientific laws that are the same across the universe and are the same yesterday and tomorrow. There is no experiment that can validate these philosophical assumptions. Also, since modern science is restricted to the search for natural explanations that can be tested, it must be neutral on the question of whether God exists. Science cannot disprove God, nor can it invoke God as part of a scientific theory, because God can't be tested.

Science is an excellent tool for learning about the natural world, but it is not a panacea that can remedy everything, nor was it ever meant to carry such a burden.

8. Isn't all of the evidence for God just "God of the gaps" reasoning? Won't science eventually explain everything that religion cannot?

A "God of the gaps" argument claims that a currently unknown feature of the natural world is proof that God exists because he is the cause of that feature. For example, ancient people who did not know what caused lighting could assume that a god caused it in order to punish mankind. These kinds of arguments for the existence of God ignore the fact that a suitable natural explanation for the phenomena we observe may eventually be discovered, and we will miss it if we rush to the conclusion "God did it!"

This happened when Isaac Newton said that the best explanation for the motion of the planets was that an intelligent agent or even angels were pushing them. We must also be wary of similar arguments today that claim certain features of the human cell, or certain organs, could not have arisen by natural means; therefore, a supernatural explanation is required. If a natural explanation is found for what we can't explain, then our evidence for God will have disappeared as the gap in our understanding is closed by scientific discovery.

Science can't prove God exists simply by pointing to natural phenomena that human beings cannot currently explain. But it also can't disprove God exists, because science cannot make judgments about entities that exist beyond the natural world.

So how does science relate to God? St. Thomas Aquinas provides us with a model of the traditional relationship between science and the use of reason to prove God exists, or what is called natural theology. Aquinas used scientific facts such as the presence of change or the regularity of movement within natural bodies as premises in *philosophical* arguments for the existence of God.

The *Catechism* states that scientific discoveries should "invite us to even greater admiration for the greatness of the Creator."[34] We should use this knowledge about how the world *is*, or what we call *science*, to ground philosophical arguments for the fundamentals of our faith, including the fundamental truth that God created the universe. We can use these arguments to demonstrate that the world has an origin outside of itself and a moral order within itself, facts that science cannot explain.

9. Hold on a minute. Hasn't science shown that something can indeed come from nothing and that moral behavior exists among chimpanzees and could have come from evolution?

Physics describes how objects move and behave in the world, but traditional physics has a limit when it comes to describing really small objects, such as electrons or quarks. For that we need quantum physics (also called quantum mechanics), which explains the nature and motion of atoms as well as the particles that make up atoms. Because these particles are so small, they can act in strange ways. For example, scientists have observed so-called "virtual particles" emerging, apparently without a cause, from an empty vacuum. If these particles can come into existence without a cause in the quantum realm, then couldn't the universe have come into being from nothing?

The problem with this argument is that a quantum vacuum is not "nothing": It is a very low state of energy that boils and froths almost like the foam on the surface of the ocean. To say our universe emerged from such a vacuum is not the same as saying it came from nothing. The quantum vacuum has properties and needs an explanation of where it came from. It will not suffice to say that the vacuum has simply existed forever, because this would not explain why our universe is of a finite age and isn't as old as the vacuum from which it came.

Philosopher and theoretical physicist David Albert of Columbia University wrote in the *New York Times* how physicists are not solving any mysteries when they try to use the spontaneous emergence of virtual particles from vacuums to explain the origin of the universe. Albert writes, "[N]one of this amounts to anything even remotely in the neighborhood of a creation from nothing."[35]

It is impossible to provide a scientific explanation of how the universe emerged from pure nothing, because scientific explanations involve the use of natural laws and processes. However, what could the scientific explanation be for the entire universe, which comprises all of space, time, matter, and energy? There can't be one, because any law or scientific process one uses to explain why the universe came from nothing would be a part of the universe you're trying to explain! Instead, the explanation for the universe's origin from nothing would have to be a supernatural explanation, an explanation that transcends matter, energy, space, and time—in other words, what we call God.

What about morality coming from evolution and being observed in primates? Primatologist Jane Goodall claims that chimpanzees exhibit a sense of fairness and that when two or more begin to quarrel over food, for instance, other chimps intervene and divide what they are fighting over.[36] But this "sharing" is merely a way to stop a potentially violent situation from escalating and so is more self-centered than other-directed. The most we can conclude from these observations is that chimpanzees know that cooperation can yield better results for everyone, not that morality itself is merely a product of evolution. Even a chimp can figure out that half a prize is better than none at all. But morality is about doing what's *right*, not about doing what is most efficient or beneficial.

Also, if we really thought chimps were moral creatures, then why don't we say chimps that maul people's faces are evil? We say those chimps are operating on instinct and don't deserve blame, because they didn't choose their behavior. But we *would* blame and condemn humans as evil should they choose to maul someone's face.

In his book *The Atheist's Guide to Reality*, philosopher Alex Rosenberg accepts that it would be radically unlikely for humans to randomly evolve behaviors that also happened to correspond with objective moral rules that exist independently of human beings in an abstract realm (rules like "It is wrong to torture children because you enjoy hearing their screams"). As a result, Rosenberg is a nihilist who says that morality is simply a human convention and has no real existence of its own.[37] But if moral facts really do exist, if some things really are wrong even if they offer evolutionary advantage for our species (such as parents' drowning disabled infants), then this points to the existence of an objective grounding for morality that does not change and provides the source of our moral obligations—in other words, what we call God.

10. How can you trust the Bible when the book of Genesis contradicts the theory of evolution by

saying the world was created in six twenty-four-hour days 6,000 years ago?

Even though some Christians who call themselves "young-Earth creationists" claim the Bible teaches that the universe is 6,000 to 10,000 years old, based on the ages of people listed in the genealogies in the Old Testament, the Bible never states that the Earth or the universe is of a certain age. The most famous attempt to date the creation event in this way comes from the seventeenth-century Anglican archbishop James Ussher, who said the world was created in the year 4004 B.C. on the night before Sunday, October 23. In contrast to Ussher's exactness, the First Vatican Council requires only that Catholics believe "the world and all things which are contained in it, both spiritual and material, as regards their whole substance, have been produced by God from nothing."[38]

While Genesis can be read as a literal explication of God's creating the world in six twenty-four-hour days (a view held by many of the Church Fathers), throughout Church history there has been an alternative interpretation that has come to be called the *framework interpretation*. This is the view that the six days of creation do not consist of a literal, chronological description of events. They are instead a topical way of describing how God created the world. In the first three days God creates the realms where creation will reside (the sky, the waters, the land, and vegetation); then God fills those realms in the next three days (with the lights in the sky, the birds and fish, and the land animals).

This interpretation explains passages such as Genesis 1:14-18, which describes God's creating the sun on day four even though he had created the light on day one. St. Augustine argued in his commentary on Genesis that God created the world in an instant but that six days were used to describe it because, according to Greek mathematicians, six is a perfect number representing how the world is perfected in the act of creation. The *Catechism* states, "Scripture presents the work of the Creator symbolically as a succession of six days of divine 'work,' concluded by the 'rest' of the seventh day."[39]

The fact that a nonliteral interpretation of Genesis was proposed nearly 1,500 years before Darwin shows that such an interpretation is not a desperate attempt to explain away Genesis in light of the findings of evolutionary biology. In fact, after Darwin published his theory, Cardinal Henry Newman remarked in a letter to a friend, "Mr. Darwin's theory need not then to be atheistical, be it true or not; it may simply be suggesting a larger idea of Divine Prescience and Skill."[40]

The Catholic Church teaches that the first chapters of Genesis contain historical truths, but those chapters also use "simple and metaphorical language adapted to the mentality of a people but little cultured, both state the principal truths which are fundamental for our salvation, and also give a popular description of the origin of the human race and the chosen people."[41] The Church has affirmed only that Scripture infallibly teaches that God created the world from nothing by his own will and made man's immortal soul in his image. The Church has not issued an infallible interpretative judgment on the precise method God used to create the world or how long that process took. As a result, a Catholic is free to believe in either a literal view of Genesis or another interpretation that allows for a long period of time in which life evolves from a common ancestor.

In fact, in a 2007 address, Pope Benedict XVI said, "[T]here are so many scientific proofs in favor of evolution which appears to be a reality we can see and which enriches our knowledge of life and being as such. But on the other, the doctrine of evolution does not answer every query, especially the great philosophical question: where does everything come from? And how did everything start which ultimately led to man? I believe this is of the utmost importance."[42]

According to Pope Pius XII's encyclical *Humani Generis*, a Catholic is free to believe that life (including the bodies of modern human beings) was formed via the evolutionary process. Catholics are simply not free to believe that our souls were part of the evolutionary process, since the soul is immortal and immaterial, meaning it cannot evolve but must be created directly by God within each human person.

11. How do Catholics view intelligent design?

Proponents of intelligent design (known as ID) claim that science can detect whether an intelligent agent designed certain features of the natural world. For example, if you walked across the beach and saw the seashells arranged to spell "Sara, will you marry me?" you would probably assume that the shells didn't wind up that way on the beach by sheer chance. In the same way, ID advocates claim, some features in biology have these same markers of design (or intentional, specified patterns) that we can detect scientifically. While they usually do not claim to know the identity of the intelligent designer, most ID advocates believe the designer is the Judeo-Christian God. ID advocates differ among themselves over whether life evolved or was created directly by God several thousand years ago.

The Catholic physicist and ID advocate Michael Behe claims that one can believe that all life descended naturally from a common ancestor.[43] However, Behe believes that an intelligent designer created certain microscopic biological structures that are too complicated to be explained by natural theories of biological development. The most common examples cited by intelligent design advocates include:

- "Miniature machines in the cell" such as the bacterial flagellum
- The immune system and blood clotting cascade
- DNA and the genetic code

Intelligent design became better known after a 2005 federal court judge deemed a Pennsylvania school board's decision to offer an intelligent design textbook as well as a publicly read disclaimer related to ID and evolution to be an unconstitutional endorsement of religion.[44] The Catholic Church has not issued a document nor given any specific teaching related to intelligent design. It has also not encouraged school boards to teach intelligent design in public high school biology classrooms. Catholics are free to believe God created the world in this way and that evidence for the existence of God can be found through intelligent design arguments.

However, there is some controversy within the Catholic community about the merits of the intelligent design argument. While some Catholics like Behe support intelligent design, other Catholics argue that intelligent design represents a mechanistic view of nature that is incompatible with a traditional Thomistic view of the world. They claim that Aquinas viewed nature being directed as a whole toward an intelligent end or goal. As a result, there would be no reason for God to intervene and specially create certain natural parts that make up the world.[45]

In 2004 the International Theological Commission, headed by then Cardinal Joseph Ratzinger, issued a statement on the origins question that referred to intelligent design: "A growing body of scientific critics of neo-Darwinism point to evidence of design (e.g., biological structures that exhibit specified complexity) that, in their view, cannot be explained in terms of a purely contingent process and that neo-Darwinians have ignored or misinterpreted. The nub of this currently lively disagreement involves scientific observation and generalization concerning whether the available data support inferences of design or chance, and cannot be settled by theology."[46]

12. How can you say God created the universe when science has proven that humans are just an insignificant speck within it?

Some critics claim that if God existed, then the universe would not be 13.7 billion years old or 93 billion light-years across. Hasn't science shown that the universe was not created for us?

The problem with this argument is that science can show us only the universe's dimensions; it cannot reveal any meaning or lack of meaning inherent in those dimensions. In response to this argument, the believer can simply ask, "Why can't God choose to create a magnificent and grand universe like ours?" The critic might respond that God wouldn't use such an inefficient process like cosmic and biological evolution and would instead create life instantaneously.

But creating a grand universe could be "inefficient" only if the creator were limited in time and resources. For example, after I completed my graduate studies, I drove across the country without stopping, because I didn't have a lot of time or money to spare (especially after draining my student loans). But if I had six months before I was to start my job and had just received a large inheritance, I might have gone on a long, scenic trip instead. In the same way, since God has unlimited time and resources, he has no problem making a grand cosmos for human beings. It's not as if God loses track of us in the expansive universe he created. Moreover, the human brain is the most complex thing in the universe, so why not think that God made a grand universe for such brains to explore?

How does the critic know with such confidence that God would *not* create a universe like ours? Suppose God made a very tiny universe with only our solar system in it. Would the typical atheist think that such a world proves God exists? He might just as plausibly argue that if God existed, surely he would have created something grander. A small and simple universe, he might argue, is precisely what we would expect if it simply popped into existence from nothing, without a cause. As C.S. Lewis put it, "We treat God as the policeman in the story treated the suspect; whatever he does will be used in evidence against him."[47]

Finally, if God chose to create human life through the evolutionary process, billions of years would be required for the process to culminate in the emergence of human beings. If the universe were static during that time, it would collapse due to the strength of gravity. Only an expanding universe that eventually becomes billions of light-years in diameter would allow the universe to be life-permitting for the time required for intelligent life to evolve.

Other critics claim that Copernicus's discovery that the Earth revolved around the sun dethroned the special place human beings possessed at the center of a geocentric, God-created universe. However, the reason the Earth resided at the center of the universe in the older, geocentric model was not because it was special. It was because it was basically just heavy junk.

According to Aristotle's view of the world, heavier materials such as Earth would fall closer to the center of the universe. Earth was considered the heaviest of the four elements, followed by water, fire, and air. It would make sense that our planet would form in the basin of the universe, where all the dirt collected, while the more glorified stars made of light and fire would exist higher up in the universe. In his commentary on Aristotle, St. Thomas Aquinas wrote, "[I]n the whole universe, just as the earth which is contained by all, being in the middle, is the most material and ignoble among bodies, so the outermost sphere is most formal and most noble."[48] Far from making human beings insignificant, later astronomical advances have liberated human beings from residing in the most "ignoble" spot of the universe.

In conclusion, neither the location of human beings in the universe nor the size of the universe they inhabit constitutes evidence—much less proof—that God did not create the universe.

13. Hasn't science proven there is no such thing as a soul?

In order to answer this question we must answer a prior question: "What do we mean by the word *soul*?" When many people hear the word *soul*, they think of a kind of ghost that looks just like us (it's usually even wearing the same clothes the person's body wore prior to death) as depicted in movies or cartoons. The soul is who we really are, and the body is just a kind of shell we operate in and then escape from after death.

Some modern critics say that this concept of the soul cannot exist, because science has shown that a person's personality can be affected by injuries to the brain. For example, due to a terrible work-related accident, a nineteenth-century railroad worker named Phineas Gage had a railroad spike lodged in his brain. Gage miraculously survived, but his friends and family noticed that his personality changed abruptly after the incident and he seemed like a "different person." Critics argue that if a person is a soul, then how could his personality change just because his body is damaged? They conclude that a person is not a soul but is simply his brain and that when the brain perishes, so does the person.

The truth is that a human being is not merely a brain, nor is he only a soul. A human being is a *composite* of soul and body. The soul is the "form" of the body, or it is what makes a living human body different than a dead human body, even though both bodies could contain living cells.[49] Upon the death of the physical body, the soul survives, because it is not composed of any material parts. The soul is directly created by God and is immortal. The Church teaches that at the end of time God will resurrect our human bodies, and our souls will be reunited with those bodies.

Because our souls and bodies are so intimately joined, what happens to one will affect the other. The personality change of Phineas Gage or anyone else can be explained without discarding belief in an immaterial soul. The soul continues to animate the body and provide the foundation for rational thought. However, if the body—in this case, the brain—is damaged, the soul may not be able to manifest itself properly or even at all.

Consider a car whose axle is warped so that the car always veers to the left. You might think the person driving the car is a bad driver, but he may simply be unable to compensate for the damage to the vehicle he is driving—just as the soul cannot compensate for the damage to the body it is united to and display a proper rational function.

Also, when scientists show that certain portions of the brain become active or emit electrical impulses during particular actions, they have not proven that these actions or thoughts are *caused* by the material interactions in the brain. All they have proven is that there is a *correlation* between certain actions or thoughts and electrical signals in the brain. This correlation does not rule out the possibility that the soul uses the body in order to act or think about certain ideas.

The question of whether or not an immaterial soul exists is a not scientific question; it is instead a philosophical or a theological one. In fact, there are powerful philosophical arguments in favor of the existence of the soul, because human beings are capable of *choosing* to believe certain things. If we were merely our brains and were subject to how the molecules in our brains randomly collide with one another, then we would have no reason to trust any of the randomly generated beliefs our brains generate, including the belief that human beings do not have souls.

14. Why is the Church opposed to stem cell research that could provide medical breakthroughs for millions of people?

Stem cells are a kind of cell that can reproduce and become any other type of cell (e.g., nerve, muscle, bone).

They are thought to be capable of healing people with a wide variety of ailments, from Parkinson's disease to muscular dystrophy, because they can grow and replace any kind of missing cells in a person's body. So why does the Catholic Church oppose research that seems as if it can yield such promising results?

The Church is not opposed to valid medical research that can help heal the sick. In fact, caring for the sick and disabled is considered a work of mercy, and the Church promotes this work to such an extent that it is one of the largest nongovernmental providers of health care in the world. So while it is important to heal the sick, Catholics understand that we must not use immoral means to do so, and even secular medical organizations understand this is not an "anti-science" attitude. The National Institutes of Health publishes a list of protocols for human test subjects in order to keep them from being harmed or exploited.[50] Most people do not consider these regulations to be "anti-scientific," because human welfare is more important than scientific progress.

We must be clear on this issue, since most people have it wrong: The Catholic Church does not oppose stem cell research. The Vatican regularly hosts a conference on how *adult* stem cells, which are obtained from sources such as the umbilical cord, can be used to treat hundreds of different diseases.[51] The Church opposes only *embryonic* stem cell research, because human embryos must be destroyed in order to harvest these cells.

The scientific community is in agreement that human embryos are biological human beings. This fact is attested to in medical textbooks such as *Human Embryology and Teratology,* which states, "Although human life is a continuous process, fertilization is a critical landmark because, under ordinary circumstances, a new, genetically distinct human organism is thereby formed."[52] A human embryo's lack of development no more gives us the right to kill it for medical experimentation than the lack of development present in newborns or the disabled gives us any right to kill them.

But what about human embryos that have been abandoned in cold-storage facilities? If these embryos will die anyway, then why not perform research on them? It is a tragedy that human beings will be "thrown away" and that there are no immediate and moral means to remedy this situation. But this does not give us a license to worsen the situation by using these human beings' bodies for medical experiments.

Instead, these human beings should be granted a dignified death, and no more embryonic human beings should be created. The situation could be likened to the plight of starving children in developing nations who may die anyway because of our inability to provide them with foreign aid. This tragic situation would not justify our using these children for medical experiments and then discarding them as medical waste. The ecclesial document *Dignitatis Personae* addressed this topic: "Proposals to use these embryos for research or for the treatment of disease are obviously unacceptable because they treat the embryos as mere 'biological material' and result in their destruction. The proposal to thaw such embryos without reactivating them and use them for research, as if they were normal cadavers, is also unacceptable."[53]

15. Why doesn't the Church accept the American Psychological Association's conclusion that homosexuality is not disordered?

According to the American Psychological Association, "[L]esbian, gay, and bisexual orientations are not disorders. Research has found no inherent association between any of these sexual orientations and psychopathology. Both heterosexual behavior and homosexual behavior are normal aspects of human sexuality. Both have been documented in many different cultures and historical eras."[54] This assessment stands in stark contrast with that of the Catholic Church, which teaches, "Homosexual acts are intrinsically disordered. They are contrary to the natural law. They close the sexual act to the gift of life. They do not proceed from a genuine affective and sexual complementarity. Under no circumstances can they be approved."[55]

Is this a clear-cut case of religion contradicting science? It is not, because science can provide insight only into the *factual* questions related to human sexuality and not the *moral* questions, because science cannot determine morality. The Church does agree with the APA on the fact that homosexuality "has taken a great variety of forms through the centuries and in different cultures."[56] The APA and the Church also agree on the scientific question of what causes homosexual orientation. The APA says, "[N]o findings have emerged that permit scientists to conclude that sexual orientation is determined by any particular factor or factors," and the Church says of same-sex attraction, "Its psychological genesis remains largely unexplained."

However, when the APA says homosexuality is "normal," it is making a moral judgment and not a factual one. Consider individuals with a homosexual orientation and those who are ambidextrous: Members of both groups comprise less than 2 percent of the population, making them statistically "abnormal," but this does not mean that either condition is *morally* abnormal.[57] Morality involves questions related to how human beings ought to treat one another, and science simply cannot answer those questions. Each person who approaches the question of how humans should treat one another brings with him a set of nonscientific values that he uses to answer the question. For example, the APA simply uses the standard that an action is moral as long as it doesn't lead to "psychopathology," but there is no uniform definition of what that term means and no scientific way to determine what a psychopath is.

Typically, sexual acts that cause harm and are performed without a participant's consent are considered a sign of psychopathology (hence the term *psychopath*). But under this view of sexual morality, there is no principled reason to consider consensual adult incest, polygamy, or even sexual relations between humans and animals (so long as the animals are not injured) to be immoral, because those behaviors are not "psychopathic."

In contrast, the Church's view of sexuality teaches that human beings and their bodies were designed to function in a certain way. This view can better explain the wrongness of sexual disorders that do not "hurt" anyone and can also explain the wrongness of homosexual acts. People of the same sex were not designed to have sex with one another, because sex was designed to be the full and free gift of a man and woman to one another with the potential to create new human life.

So does the Church simply abandon people who experience same-sex attraction? Of course not. God calls all people to be a part of his Church, regardless of their desires and personal orientations. A person is not committing a sin simply by having a homosexual orientation any more than a person sins by having any number of sinful desires. It is acting upon those desires that constitutes disorder and sin.

The *Catechism* states, "The number of men and women who have deep-seated homosexual tendencies is not negligible. This inclination, which is objectively disordered, constitutes for most of them a trial. They must be accepted with respect, compassion, and sensitivity. Every sign of unjust discrimination in their regard should be avoided. These persons are called to fulfill God's will in their lives and, if they are Christians, to unite to the sacrifice of the Lord's Cross the difficulties they may encounter from their condition. Homosexual persons are called to chastity. By the virtues of self-mastery that teach them inner freedom, at times by the support of disinterested friendship, by prayer and sacramental grace, they can and should gradually and resolutely approach Christian perfection."[58]

16. Why does the Church oppose fertility treatments that can help infertile couples have a baby?

Every year millions of couples receive the diagnosis that they have infertility issues or are unable to conceive a child. Such individuals may fall into depression or suffer from other physical and emotional problems related to this diagnosis. It is not surprising that many of these couples turn to assisted reproductive technologies in order to conceive children. If the Catholic Church believes that the creation of human beings is good, then why would it oppose these fertility treatments?

The Church does not oppose all assisted reproductive technologies. In fact, organizations like the Pope Paul VI Institute in Omaha, Nebraska, have conducted extensive research into medical practices that treat the root causes of infertility without violating the sanctity of the marital act. Examples of this include the use of NaPro reproductive technologies and natural family planning to help couples conceive children during a woman's fertile period. In addition, fertility drugs that stimulate ovum or sperm production, and surgical procedures that repair damaged organs are valid medical procedures, because they treat illnesses and restore the proper functioning of the body. The Church promotes procedures that *repair* the body but not procedures that *replace* sexual union, such as in vitro fertilization (IVF), the process of creating a human embryo outside of the body and then implanting it within the woman.

One reason the Church opposes in vitro fertilization is that it is dangerous for the child and treats the child and the couple as if they were part of a manufacturing process and not a family. In most IVF cases, multiple embryos are created in a laboratory (from genetic materials that may have been obtained through illicit means such as masturbation), and then only some are implanted in a woman's womb. Through pre-implantation genetic diagnosis, embryos with genetic abnormalities (such as Down syndrome) can be screened and destroyed along with other unwanted embryos. However, not even all the embryos that are implanted survive, because the extra implanted embryos are often aborted (which is referred to euphemistically as "selective reduction"). Some doctors even offer to abort these extra embryos because they are of an unwanted sex.

Finally, even if IVF could be practiced in a way in which embryos were not destroyed, it would still separate the unitive and procreative aspects of human sexuality. Children created in this way, while still being made in the image of God and possessing intrinsic value, would not be the product of the free and total gift of a husband and wife. They would instead be the manufactured result of a laboratory process involving dozens of strangers.

Many of these human embryos are never implanted but are preserved in cold-storage facilities. In light of the tragedy of millions of human embryos being left in this unnatural condition, some Catholics have wondered whether the Church permits adopting these frozen embryos (sometimes called "snowflake babies"). The question of adopting snowflake babies is a morally complex one for Catholics. On the one hand, it is a laudable goal to provide a safe haven in the womb for frozen human embryos that would most likely be destroyed. On the other hand, approving the adoption of these embryos may encourage more use of IVF and treat these children as commodities and not persons.

In the instruction *Dignitatis Personae*, the Church's Congregation for the Doctrine of the Faith praised the intentions of those who seek to adopt frozen embryos in order to benefit the children themselves and not use them as a means to "have children." However, the magisterium also realizes that this is not a morally acceptable solution to the problem of frozen, orphaned embryos. The document says, "The proposal that these embryos could be put at the disposal of infertile couples as a treatment for infertility is not ethically acceptable for the same reasons which make artificial heterologous procreation illicit as well as any form of surrogate motherhood; this practice would also lead to other problems of a medical, psychological, and legal nature."[59]

17. Why doesn't the Church support the use of contraceptives that have been scientifically proven to reduce rates of unintended pregnancies as well as sexually transmitted diseases?

As the previous questions about science and morality have indicated, just because something *can* be done doesn't mean that it *should* be done. The government could, for example, place chemicals in public drinking water in order to reduce fertility rates to more manageable levels, but most people would consider that immoral. A person should not be forced to use contraceptives in order to achieve some "greater good," because procreation is a basic human right.

If the involuntary use of contraceptives is immoral, then it is also possible that the voluntary use of contraceptives could also be immoral. After all, some actions are wrong independent of whether or not they are voluntary. For example, forcing women to participate in pornographic videos is wrong, but so is making the same video with willing actresses, because it devalues women and invites others to view them as objects instead of persons made in God's image.

The Church's opposition to contraceptives would be "anti-science" in nature only if it disagreed with the scientific facts related to contraceptives. The Church accepts that contraceptives work with varying degrees of success at preventing unintended pregnancies and, in the case of barrier methods like condoms, at preventing the spread of sexually transmitted diseases. While the exact usefulness of contraceptives may be disputed, their general nature is not, and so this is not an issue of the Church's standing against scientific progress. The larger issue is whether it is right or wrong to purposefully suppress or damage a natural part of the human body. This is a question of morality, not science.

The Church teaches that marriage is a union of man and woman who have given literally every part of themselves to one other. Every act of sexual intercourse renews the vows of marriage and is a total gift of each spouse to the other person. Along with renewing their vow to be faithful, the couple also renews their vow to be open to life in every act of marital intercourse. Of course, some critics will object to this and claim that the Church wants every couple to have eighteen children. But saying that every act of intercourse must be open to life does not mean that a couple cannot space their children and plan their families.

God has given women times when they are not fertile, and couples may have intercourse during those times, knowing a child will probably not be created. A person committed to science will appreciate that the effectiveness of natural family planning, in some cases as high as 98 percent, has been demonstrated in peer-reviewed medical journals.[60]

18. Does the Church believe that some vaccines are bad because they come from "aborted babies"?

One dilemma that arises in bioethics is the use of research that entails immoral or even evil means. For example, scientists wrestle with what to do with the medical research compiled in Nazi concentration camps that can provide valuable insights (such as effective rewarming techniques for hypothermia victims that were developed by submerging prisoners in freezing water until they lost consciousness). When it comes to vaccines, a dilemma arises when one considers that some vaccines came into existence through experiments performed on aborted unborn children.

In order to create a vaccine against a particular virus, scientists will create cell lines, or new cells that contain the virus. Scientists will sometimes create conditions that weaken the virus, such as keeping the cell lines in an environment that has a lower temperature than the human body. This allows humans who are exposed to it to develop immunity without suffering the symptoms associated with the disease the virus causes.

However, some of the cell lines scientists use for the vaccination process came from aborted fetuses. During the 1960s an epidemic of rubella spread throughout Europe and the United States. Pregnant women who had contracted the virus often gave birth to children with cataracts and other birth defects. Some pregnant women decided to abort their children rather than bear them with these defects. One of these aborted fetuses was sent to Stanley Plotkin of the Wistar Institute in Philadelphia, who isolated the virus in the fetus's kidney.

The cell lines used to create today's rubella vaccine are copies of the cells that once existed in an aborted child. These modern cells were never a part of an unborn child, and vaccines do not contain "pieces" of aborted babies. But like the benefits derived from unethical Nazi research, Plotkin's research involved the unjust act of killing an innocent person. This raises ethical dilemmas about whether or not the cell line derived from his research (which is now called WI-38) can be used legitimately to create vaccines. While some vaccines that were derived from aborted children can be substituted with ethical alternatives derived from different strains, at this time there are no alternative vaccines for rubella, chicken pox, or hepatitis A.

The Catholic Church has decided that the good of protecting the public from a dangerous disease outweighs the evil associated with vaccine strains like WI-38. The Pontifical Academy for Life stated in a 2005 letter, "The lawfulness of the use of these vaccines should not be misinterpreted as a declaration of the lawfulness of their production, marketing and use, but is to be understood as being a passive material cooperation and, in its mildest and remotest sense, also active, morally justified as an *extrema ratio* due to the necessity to provide for the good of one's children and of the people who come in contact with the children (pregnant women)."

The Catholic Church is not against the use of vaccines and affirms the scientific consensus that they are an effective means of combating infectious diseases. The Church even obligates parents to use vaccines, when it is ethical and moral to do so, in order to protect their children from harm. However, the Church recognizes that a "remote, material" cooperation with evil occurs when using vaccines that are derived from aborted children. Since conscientious Catholics do not act with the intention of causing abortions to continue (or what is called formal cooperation), the Church allows the use of vaccines due to the tremendous evil that would occur were they not used.

Although the Church places a heavy moral obligation upon Catholics to use vaccines that were not derived from aborted fetuses, if that is not possible, they may ethically use vaccines derived originally from aborted children. It is recommended, however, that parents complain to vaccine providers as a kind of "conscientious objection" in hopes that more ethical alternatives can be developed in the future.

19. How do you explain the fact that the majority of scientists are atheists?

Ninety-three percent of the members of the National Academy of Sciences, one of the most elite scientific organizations in the United States, do not believe in God.[61] Is it an argument against the truth of religious belief that so many of these intelligent people don't believe in God? I don't think so, and here's why.

First, the National Academy of Sciences represents a small number of scientists. The Academy itself comprises only about 2,000 members, while there are more than two million scientists employed in the United States as a whole.[62] This means that the NAS represents about one-tenth of 1 percent of all scientists in the nation. Using the 93 percent statistic to prove scientists are overwhelmingly atheists would be inaccurate. A more accurate description comes from the Pew Research Center, which reported in 2009 that 51 percent of scientists believe that God or some higher power exists, while 41 percent of scientists reject both of those concepts. In addition, while only 2 percent of the general population identifies as atheist, 17 percent of scientists identify with that term.[63]

However, we can't resolve the question of God's existence by relying on the personal opinions of scientists, because the existence of God is not a scientific question. Science restricts itself to searching for natural explanations of observed phenomena. Natural scientists (such as the biologists, chemists, and physicists that make up the Pew study) are no more equipped to make conclusions about God than they are equipped to make conclusions about economics, history, literature, or philosophy. Since the question of God is philosophical in nature, scientists who investigate it are no more qualified than any other educated laymen.

Finally, it may not be science that turns people into atheists but atheism that turns people into scientists. In Elaine Ecklund's book *Science vs. Religion: What Scientists Really Think*, she demonstrates through various interviews that many scientists reject religion for personal reasons prior to becoming scientists as opposed to rejecting religion on scientific grounds.

There is no reason to think that science has an inherent tendency to lead someone to reject religious beliefs. In fact, while in the general population it is older people who tend to be religious and younger people who tend to be nonreligious, the reverse is true among scientists. According to the Pew Research Center, while fewer than half of the scientists over the age of 65 believe in God or a higher power, a full two-thirds of scientists under the age of 34 believe in God or a higher power, with the majority of that group believing in God by an almost two-to-one margin.[64] Rather than retreat from science in order to protect the faith of our children, we should encourage our children to become scientists in order to protect the faith of other people!

20. What have religious people ever done for science?

In recent years, it's true, some of the world's most prominent scientists have been outspoken about their atheism. However, as I explained in the previous question, the majority of practicing scientists do not call themselves atheists. Furthermore, some of the most famous scientists in history have been people of faith:

- The medieval saint Albert the Great is considered the patron saint of natural science because of his diligence in cataloging all of the known scientific discoveries of his time.
- The thirteenth-century Franciscan friar Roger Bacon emphasized the importance of experiments in science and helped gather research about light and

optics, which was later advanced in the same century by the archbishop of Canterbury John Peckham.

- In 1543 Nicolaus Copernicus, who held a degree in Catholic canon law, became the first person to advance a comprehensive description of the heliocentric universe.
- The seventeenth-century bishop Nicholas Steno was one of the founders of modern geology and provided many valuable insights into stratigraphy (the study of rock layers).
- In 1740 the Scottish Benedictine monk Andrew Gordon became the first person to build an electric motor.
- The nineteenth-century Augustinian friar Gregor Mendel's experiments with pea plants resulted in what are known as the Mendelian "laws of inheritance," and Mendel himself is considered one of the founders of the science of genetics.
- The Belgian priest Georges Lemaître's discoveries in the early part of the twentieth century would earn him the moniker "Father of the Big Bang theory."

Finally, it's important to remember that many of the scientific discoveries in the Middle Ages were possible only because the Church financially supported scientists who helped the faithful more clearly understand God's creation. For example, in order to calculate the correct date of Easter, the Church invested large sums of money and man-hours into studying astronomy.

According to historian J.L. Heilbron, "The Roman Catholic Church gave more financial and social support to the study of astronomy for over six centuries, from the recovery of ancient learning during the late Middle Ages into the Enlightenment, than any other, and, probably, all other, institutions."[65]

About the Author

Trent Horn is an apologist and speaker for Catholic Answers. He specializes in pro-life issues as well as outreach to atheists and agnostics. He holds a master's degree in theology from Franciscan University of Steubenville.

Endnotes

1   Colin A. Russell, "The Conflict of Science and Religion," in Gary
     B. Ferngren, ed., *Science & Religion: A Historical Introduction*
     (Baltimore: Johns Hopkins University Press, 2002), 7-8.

2   The term "Dark Ages" is not used by professional historians, but
     comes from the fourteenth-century historian Petrarch, who used
     it to contrast medieval society with Roman culture, which he
     wished society would return to.

3   David Lindberg, "That the Rise of Christianity Was Responsible
     for the Demise of Ancient Science," in Ronald L. Numbers,
     Galileo Goes to Jail and Other Myths About Science and Religion
     (Harvard University Press, Cambridge, 2009), 9.

4   Socrates Scholasticus, *Church History* 5.22. This antagonism
     no doubt arose because Socrates embraced the heresy of
     Novationism, which denied apostates readmission into the
     Church.

5   "The glory of the Alexandrian Library is a dim memory. Its last
     remnants were destroyed soon after Hypatia's death. It was as if
     the entire civilization had undergone some self-inflicted brain
     surgery, and most of its memories, discoveries, ideas and passions
     were extinguished irrevocably": Carl Sagan, *Cosmos* (Toronto:
     Random House Publishing, 1980), 279. It's true that the Patriarch
     of Alexandria Theophilus closed the temples in Alexandria in
     391 and those temples were later destroyed. One of the temples
     was called the Serapeum, and while it was rumored that some
     remnants of the library were located there, no one knows how
     many, or if any, books were present. The main argument against

there being books in the Serapeum is that historians living at that time, such as Paulus Orosius, do not mention a library being present in the Temple.

6 Plutarch, *Life of Caesar* 49:6.

7 Sagan, 278.

8 Michael Shank, "That the Medieval Christian Church Suppressed the Growth of Science," in Numbers, *Galileo Goes to Jail*, 21-22.

9 Paul Johnson, *The Renaissance: A Short History* (Modern Library, New York, 2002), 7.

10 Pliny the Elder, *The Natural History*, chap. 64, "Of the Form of the Earth."

11 St. Basil the Great, *The Hexaemeron*, Homily 9.

12 Andrew Dickson White, *A History of the Warfare Between Science and Theology in Christendom*, pt. 1, chap. 2.

13 David C. Lindberg and Ronald L. Numbers, "Beyond War and Peace: A Reappraisal of the Encounter between Christianity and Science," *Church History* (Cambridge University Press) 1986, 55 (3): 338–354.

14 Robert G. Ingersoll, "Individuality" (1873).

15 James Hannam, "Science Versus Christianity?" Patheos, May 18, 2010, http://www.patheos.com/Resources/Additional-Resources/Science-Versus-Christianity.html.

16 White, *A History of the Warfare Between Science and Theology in Christendom*, chap. 13, sec. 5.

17 July 17, 2006, U.S. Senate session regarding the *Stem Cell Research Enhancement Act of 2005; in Congressional Record 152, no. 93 (July 17, 2006), http://www.gpo.gov/fdsys/pkg/CREC-2006-07-17/html/CREC-2006-07-17-pt1-PgS7569-3.htm.*

18 Andre Thevene, "Guy de Chauliac (1300-1370): The Father of Surgery," *Annals of Vascular Surgery* 7, no. 2, p. 208.

19 Katharine Park, "That the Medieval Church Prohibited Human Dissection," in Numbers, *Galileo Goes to Jail and Other Myths About Science and Religion*, 47-48.

20 Roland Baintun. *Hunted Heretic: The Life and Death of Michael Servetus 1511-1533* (Providence: Blackstone Editions, 2005), 140-141.

21 This is a predominant theme. See Michael White, *The Pope and the Heretic: The True Story of Giordano Bruno, the Man Who Dared to Defy the Roman Inquisition* (New York: HarperCollins, 2002).

22 White, *A History of the Warfare Between Science and Theology in Christendom*, chap. 3, sec. 2.

23 Sheila Rabin, "Nicolaus Copernicus," in Edward N. Zalta, ed., *The Stanford Encyclopedia of Philosophy,* Fall 2010 ed., http://plato. stanford.edu/archives/fall2010/entries/copernicus/.

24 William Turner, "Giordano Bruno," *Catholic Encyclopedia*, vol. 3 (New York: Robert Appleton Company, 1908), http://www. newadvent.org/cathen/03016a.htm.

25 Stephen Hawking, *A Brief History of Time* (New York: Bantam Books, 1996), 120.

26 It should be noted that the book was never officially banned, but it was placed on the Index of Prohibited Books pending revisions that made it clear that the book's thesis was a tentative hypothesis and not a widely accepted theory.

27 This is found in the ambassador's February 13 and April 16 letters in 1633 to the King of Tuscany.

28 Pope John Paul II, *L'Osservatore Romano*, November 4, 1992.

29 CCC 283.

30 The First Vatican Council teaches in canon 5, "If anyone does not confess that the world and all things which are contained in it, both spiritual and material, were produced, according to their whole substance, out of nothing by God; or holds that God did not create by his will free from all necessity, but as necessarily as he necessarily loves himself; or denies that the world was created for the glory of God: let him be anathema."

31 Jastrow. *God and the Astronomers*, 107.

32 St. Thomas Aquinas, *Summa Contra Gentiles* 1:64.

33 Stephen Hawking and Leonard Mlodinow, *The Grand Design* (New York: Random House, 2010), 1.

34 CCC 283.

35 David Albert. "A Universe from Nothing," *New York Times*, March 23, 2012, http://www.nytimes.com/2012/03/25/books/review/a-universe-from-nothing-by-lawrence-m-krauss.html?_r=0.

36 Darby Proctor, et al., "Chimpanzees Play the Ultimatum Game," PNAS 110, no. 6, published ahead of print on January 14, 2013, doi:10.1073/pnas.1220806110.

37 Alex Rosenberg. *The Atheist's Guide to Reality* (New York: W.W. Norton Company, 2011).

38 *Canons on God the Creator of All Things*, canon 5.

39 CCC 337.

40 John Henry Newman, Letter to J. Walker of Scarborough, May 22, 1868, *The Letters and Diaries of John Henry Newman* (Oxford: Clarendon Press, 1973).

41 Pope Pius XII, *Humani Generis* 38.

42 Pope Benedict XVI, Meeting of the Holy Father Benedict XVI
    with the Clergy of the Dioceses of Belluno-Feltre and Treviso,
    July 24, 2007, http://www.vatican.va/holy_father/benedict_xvi/
    speeches/2007/july/documents/hf_ben-xvi_spe_20070724_clero-
    cadore_en.html.

43 Michael Behe, *The Edge of Evolution* (New York: Free Press, 2007),
    72. Behe says, "Common descent is true" but goes on to say that a
    non-random process must exist to account for it.

44 See Tammy Kitzmiller et al. vs. Dover Area School District, 400 F.
    Supp. 2d 707 (M.D. Pa. 2005).

45 See Francis J. Beckwith, "How to Be an Anti-Intelligent Design
    Advocate," *University of St. Thomas Journal of Law and Public
    Policy* 4.1 (2010).

46 International Theological Commission, "Communion and
    Stewardship: Human Persons Created in the Image of God," 2004.

47 C.S. Lewis, *Miracles* (New York: HarperCollins, 1996), 79.

48 Thomas Aquinas, Commentary on Aristotle's "On the Heavens,"
    2:20:485. It's important to remember that the Church has never
    asserted that the physical descriptions of the universe provided
    by Aristotle or Aquinas were infallible and unchanging doctrine
    that the faithful must accept.

49 CCC 653.

50 See http://bioethics.od.nih.gov/IRB.html.

51 See http://www.news.va/en/news/vatican-adult-stem-cell-
    conference-gets-underway.

52 Ronan O'Rahilly and Fabiola Müller, *Human Embryology and
    Teratology*, 2nd ed. (New York: Wiley-Liss, 1996), 8.

53 Congregation for the Doctrine of the Faith (CDF), "Instruction *Dignitas Personae* on Certain Bioethical Questions," September 8, 2008, par. 19.

54 See http://www.apa.org/helpcenter/sexual-orientation.aspx.

55 CCC 2357.

56 Ibid.

57 A comprehensive survey conducted in 2013 by the U.S. Department of Health and Human Services found that 1.6 percent of respondents self-identified as gay or lesbian. See Ward, et al. "Sexual Orientation and Health Among U.S. Adults: National Health Interview Survey, 2013" *National Health Statistics Reports* no. 77, July 15, 2014.

58 CCC 2358-2359.

59 CDF, "Instruction *Dignitas Personae*," par. 19.

60 For example, see P. Frank-Herrmann, et al., "The Effectiveness of a Fertility Awareness Based Method to Avoid Pregnancy in Relation to a Couple's Sexual Behaviour During the Fertile Time: A Prospective Longitudinal Study," *Human Reproduction* 22, no. 5 (February 20, 2007): 1310-1319, doi:10.1093/humrep/dem003.

61 Ronald Aronson, "The New Atheists." *The Nation*, June 25, 2007.

62 See http://www.nsf.gov/statistics/nsf05313/pdf/tab2.pdf.

63 See Pew Research Forum. "Scientists and Belief" November 5, 2009, http://www.pewforum.org/2009/11/05/scientists-and-belief/.

64 Ibid.

65 J.L. Heilbron. *The Sun in the Church: Cathedrals as Solar Observatories* (Cambridge: Harvard University Press, 1999), 3.

Become part of the team.
Help support Catholic Answers.

Catholic Answers is an apostolate dedicated to serving Christ by bringing the fullness of Catholic truth to the world. We help good Catholics become better Catholics, bring former Catholics "home," and lead non-Catholics into the fullness of the Faith.

Catholic Answers neither asks for nor receives financial support from any diocese. The majority of its annual income is in the form of donations from individual supporters like you.

To make a donation by phone using your credit card, please speak with one of our customer service representatives at 888-291-8000.

To make a donation by check, please send a check payable to "Catholic Answers" to:

> Catholic Answers
> 2020 Gillespie Way
> El Cajon, CA 92020

To make a donation online, visit **catholic.com**.

TO EXPLAIN & DEFEND THE FAITH

catholic.com